OLD FASHIONED
NURSERY RHYMES

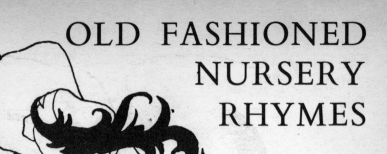

OLD FASHIONED NURSERY RHYMES

Compiled by
Jennifer Mülherin

Designed by Tom Deas

A DRAGON BOOK

Dragon
Grafton Books
A Division of the Collins Publishing Group
8 Grafton Street, London W1X 3LA

Published by Granada Publishing Limited in 1982
Reprinted 1983

Devised by Octavian Books Ltd

ISBN 0-583-30473-7

Printed and bound in Great Britain by
Collins, Glasgow

Set in Bembo

INTRODUCTION

The particular rhymes selected here are, we believe, the most popular. Almost all will be familiar, if not to the small child, at least to his parents - those responsible for keeping alive these traditional rhymes.

THERE WAS A JOLLY MILLER ONCE

There was a jolly miller once,
Lived on the river Dee;
He worked and sang from morn till night,
No lark as blithe as he.
And this the burden of his song
Forever used to be,
I care for nobody, no! not I,
And nobody cares for me.

THREE BLIND MICE

Three blind mice, see how they run!
They all ran after the farmer's wife,
Who cut off their tails with a carving knife,
Did you ever see such a thing in your life,
As three blind mice?

HICKORY, DICKORY, DOCK

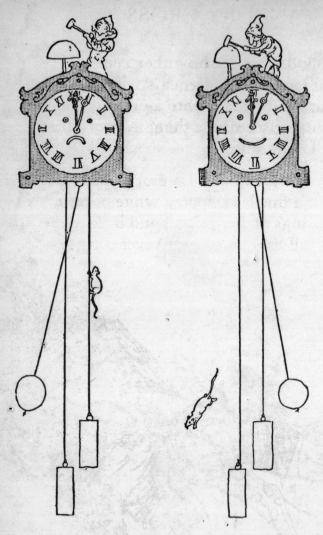

Hickory, dickory, dock,
The mouse ran up the clock.
The clock struck one,
The mouse ran down,
Hickory, dickory dock.

RIDE A COCK-HORSE
TO BANBURY CROSS

Ride a cock-horse to Banbury Cross,
To see a fine lady upon a white horse;
With rings on her fingers and bells on her toes,
She shall have music wherever she goes.

JACK BE NIMBLE

Jack be nimble,
Jack be quick,
Jack jump over
The candlestick.

THERE WAS A
LITTLE GIRL

There was a little girl, and she had a little curl
Right in the middle of her forehead;
When she was good she was very, very good,
But when she was bad she was horrid.

WHO KILLED
COCK ROBIN?

Who killed Cock Robin?
I, said the Sparrow,
With my bow and arrow,
I killed Cock Robin.

Who saw him die?
I, said the Fly,
With my little eye,
I saw him die.

Who caught his blood?
I, said the Fish,
With my little dish,
I caught his blood.

Who'll make his shroud?
I, said the Beetle,
With my thread and needle,
I'll make his shroud.

Who'll dig his grave?
I, said the Owl,
With my spade and shovel,
I'll dig his grave.

Who'll be the parson?
I, said the Rook,
With my little book,
I'll be the parson.

Who'll be the clerk?
I, said the Lark,
If it's not in the dark,
I'll be the clerk.

Who'll carry him to the grave?   Who'll carry the link?
I, said the Kite,   I, said the Linnet,
If it's not in the night,   I'll fetch it in a minute,
I'll carry him to the grave.   I'll carry the link.

Who'll be the chief mourner?
I, said the Dove,
For I mourn for my love,
I'll be the chief mourner.

Who'll bear the pall?
We, says the Wren,
Both the cock and the hen,
We'll bear the pall.

Who'll sing a psalm?
I, said the Thrush,
As she sat in a bush,
I'll sing a psalm.

Who'll toll the bell?
I, said the Bull,
Because I can pull,
So, Cock Robin, farewell.

All the birds of the air,
Fell a-sighing and a-sobbing,
When they heard the bell tolling
For poor Cock Robin.

RAIN, RAIN, GO AWAY

Rain, rain, go away,
Come again another day.

CURLY LOCKS,
CURLY LOCKS

Curly locks, Curly locks, wilt thou be mine?
Thou shalt not wash dishes, nor yet feed the swine;
But sit on a cushion and sew a fine seam,
And feed upon strawberries, sugar and cream.

BAA, BAA, BLACK SHEEP

Baa, baa, black sheep,
Have you any wool?
Yes, sir, yes, sir,
Three bags full;
One for the master,
And one for the dame,
And one for the little boy
Who lives down the lane.

GOOSEY, GOOSEY GANDER

Goosey, goosey gander,
Whither shall I wander?
Upstairs and downstairs
And in my lady's chamber.
There I met an old man
Who would not say his prayers.
I took him by the left leg
And threw him down the stairs.

A FROG HE WOULD A-WOOING GO

A frog he would a-wooing go,
Heigh ho! says Rowley,
Whether his mother would let him or no.
With a rowley, powley, gammon and spinach,
Heigh ho! Says Anthony Rowley.

So off he sets with his opera hat,
Heigh ho! says Rowley,
And on the road he met a rat.
With a rowley, powley, gammon and spinach,
Heigh ho! says Anthony Rowley.

Pray, Mister Rat, will you go with me?
Heigh ho! says Rowley,
Kind Mistress Mousey for to see?
With a rowley, powley, gammon and spinach,
Heigh ho! says Anthony Rowley.

They came to the door of Mousey's hall,
Heigh ho! says Rowley,
They gave a loud knock and they gave a loud call.
With a rowley, powley, gammon and spinach,
Heigh ho! says Anthony Rowley.

Pray, Mistress Mouse, are you within?
Heigh ho! says Rowley,
Oh yes, kind sirs, I'm sitting to spin.
With a rowley, powley, gammon and spinach,
Heigh ho! says Anthony Rowley.

Pray, Mistress Mouse, will you give us some beer?
Heigh ho! says Rowley,
For Froggy and I are fond of good cheer.
With a rowley, powley, gammon and spinach,
Heigh ho! says Anthony Rowley.

Pray, Mister Frog, will you give us a song?
Heigh ho! says Rowley,
Let it be something that's not very long.
With a rowley, powley, gammon and spinach,
Heigh ho! says Anthony Rowley.

Indeed, Mistress Mouse, replied Mister Frog,
Heigh ho! says Rowley,
A cold has made me as hoarse as a dog.
With a rowley, powley, gammon and spinach,
Heigh ho! says Anthony Rowley.

Since you have a cold, Mister Frog, Mousey said,
Heigh ho! says Rowley,
I'll sing you a song that I have just made.
With a rowley, powley, gammon and spinach,
Heigh ho! says Anthony Rowley.

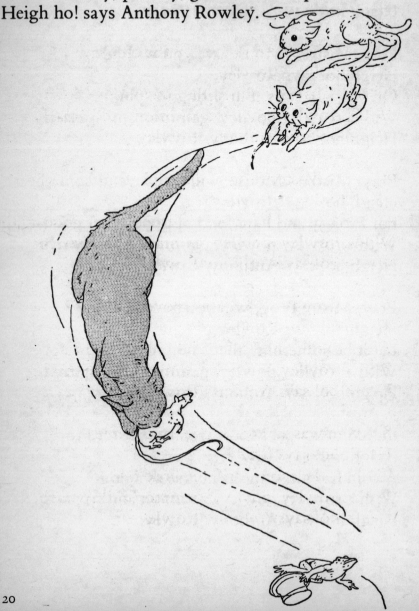

But while they were all a-merry-making,
Heigh ho! says Rowley,
A cat and her kittens came tumbling in.
With a rowley, powley, gammon and spinach,
Heigh ho! says Anthony Rowley.

The cat she seized the rat by the crown,
Heigh ho! says Rowley,
The kittens they pulled the little mouse down.
With a rowley, powley, gammon and spinach,
Heigh ho! says Anthony Rowley.

This put Mister Frog in a terrible fright,
Heigh ho! says Rowley,
He took up his hat and he wished them good-night.
With a rowley, powley, gammon and spinach,
Heigh ho! says Anthony Rowley.

But as Froggy was crossing over a brook,
Heigh ho! says Rowley,
A lily-white duck came and gobbled him up.
With a rowley, powley, gammon and spinach,
Heigh ho! says Anthony Rowley.

So there was an end of one, two, three,
Heigh ho! says Rowley,
The rat, the mouse and the little frog-ee.
With a rowley, powley, gammon and spinach,
Heigh ho! says Anthony Rowley.

SEE-SAW,
MARGERY DAW

See-Saw, Margery Daw,
Jacky shall have a new master;
Jacky shall have but a penny a day,
Because he can't work any faster.

PETER, PETER, PUMPKIN EATER

Peter, Peter, pumpkin eater,
Had a wife and couldn't keep her;
He put her in a pumpkin shell,
And there he kept her very well.

Peter, Peter, pumpkin eater,
Had another and didn't love her;
Peter learned to read and spell,
And then he loved her very well.

25

OLD KING COLE

Old King Cole
Was a merry old soul,
And a merry old soul was he;
He called for his pipe,
And he called for his bowl,
And he called for his fiddlers three.

Every fiddler he had a fiddle,
And a very fine fiddle had he;
Oh, there's none so rare,
As can compare
With King Cole and his fiddlers three.

I HAD A LITTLE PONY

I had a little pony,
His name was Dapple Grey;
I lent him to a lady
To ride a mile away.
She whipped him, she slashed him,
She rode him through the mire;
I would not lend my pony now,
For all the lady's hire.

TWINKLE, TWINKLE, LITTLE STAR

FOR WANT OF A NAIL

Twinkle, twinkle, little star,
How I wonder what you are!
Up above the moon so high,
Like a diamond in the sky.

For want of a nail, the shoe was lost,
For want of a shoe, the horse was lost,
For want of a horse, the rider was lost,
For want of a rider, the battle was lost,
For want of a battle, the kingdom was lost,
And all for the want of a horseshoe nail.

TO MARKET, TO MARKET

To market, to market, to buy a fat pig,
Home again, home again, jiggety jig.
To market, to market, to buy a fat hog,
Home again, home again, jiggety jog.

A DILLAR, A DOLLAR

A dillar, a dollar,
A ten o'clock scholar,
What makes you come so soon?
You used to come at ten o'clock,
But now you come at noon.

I DO NOT LIKE THEE, DOCTOR FELL

I do not like thee, Doctor Fell,
The reason why I cannot tell;
But this I know, and know full well,
I do not like thee, Doctor Fell.

MONDAY'S
CHILD

Monday's child is fair of face,
Tuesday's child is full of grace,
Wednesday's child is full of woe,
Thursday's child has far to go,
Friday's child is loving and giving,
Saturday's child works hard for his living,
But the child that is born on the Sabbath day
Is bonny and blithe, and good and gay.

WHAT ARE LITTLE BOYS MADE OF?

What are little boys made of?
What are little boys made of?
Frogs and snails,
And puppy-dogs' tails,
That's what little boys are made of.

What are little girls made of?
What are little girls made of?
Sugar and spice,
And all things nice,
That's what little girls are made of.

SOLOMON GRUNDY

MONDAY

TUESDAY

SOLOMON GRUNDY

WEDNESDAY

THURSDAY

Solomon Grundy,
Born on Monday,
Christened on Tuesday,
Married on Wednesday,
Took ill on Thursday,
Worse on Friday,
Died on Saturday,
Buried on Sunday,
This is the end
Of Solomon Grundy.

FRIDAY

SATURDAY

SUNDAY

HERE LIES
—
SOLOMON GRUNDY
=
SEVEN DAYS MAKE ONE WEAK

THE MAN IN
THE MOON

The man in the moon
Came tumbling down,
And asked his way to Norwich;
He went by the south,
And burnt his mouth
With supping cold plum porridge.

CLAP HANDS,
CLAP HANDS

Clap hands, clap hands,
Till father comes home;
For father's got money,
But mother's got none.

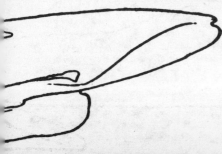

OH WHERE, OH WHERE HAS MY LITTLE DOG GONE?

Oh where, oh where has my little dog gone?
Oh where, oh where can he be?
With his ears cut short and his tail cut long,
Oh where, oh where is he?

YANKEE
DOODLE

Yankee Doodle went to town,
Riding on a pony;
He stuck a feather in his cap
And called it macaroni.

RUB-A-DUB-DUB

Rub-a-dub-dub,
Three men in a tub;
And who do you think they be?
The butcher, the baker,
The candlestick-maker;
They all jumped out of a rotten potato,
Turn'em out, knaves all three!

Mervyn Peake.

NOW I LAY ME
DOWN TO SLEEP

Now I lay me down to sleep,
I pray the Lord my soul to keep;
And if I die before I wake,
I pray the Lord my soul to take.

RING-A-RING
O'ROSES

Ring-a-ring o'roses,
A pocket full of posies,
A-tishoo! A-tishoo!
We all fall down.

BOBBY SHAFTO

Bobby Shafto's gone to sea,
Silver buckles at his knee;
He'll come back and marry me,
Bonny Bobby Shafto!

Bobby Shafto's fat and fair,
Combing down his yellow hair;
He's my love for evermore,
Bonny Bobby Shafto!

Bobby Shafto's looking out,
All his ribbons flew about;
All the ladies gave a shout,
Hey for Bobby Shafto!

TWEEDLE-DUM
AND
TWEEDLE-DEE

Tweedle-dum and Tweedle-dee
Resolved to have a battle,
For Tweedle-dum said Tweedle-dee
Had spoiled his nice new rattle.
Just then flew by a monstrous crow,
As big as a tar-barrel,
Which frightened both the heroes so,
They quite forgot their quarrel.

EARLY TO BED,
EARLY TO RISE

Early to bed and early to rise
Makes a man healthy, wealthy, and wise.

HICKETY
PICKETY, MY
BLACK HEN

Hickety Pickety, my black hen,
She lay eggs for gentlemen;
Sometimes nine, and sometimes ten,
Hickety Pickety, my black hen.

TWO LITTLE
DICKY BIRDS

Two little dicky birds sitting on a wall;
One named Peter, one named Paul.
Fly away, Peter! Fly away Paul!
Come back, Peter! Come back, Paul!

A WISE OLD OWL

A wise old owl lived in an oak;
The more he saw the less he spoke.
The less he spoke the more he heard.
Why can't we all be like that wise old bird?

ORANGES AND LEMONS

Oranges and lemons,
Say the bells of St Clement's.

You owe me five farthings,
Say the bells of St Martin's.

When will you pay me?
Say the bells at Old Bailey.

When I grow rich,
Say the bells at Shoreditch.

Pray, when will that be?
Say the bells at Stepney.

I'm sure I don't know,
Says the great bell at Bow.

Here comes a candle to light you to bed,
And here comes a chopper to chop off your head.

OLD MOTHER GOOSE

Old Mother Goose, when
She wanted to wander,
Would ride through the air
On a very find gander.

Mother Goose had a house,
'Twas built in a wood,
Where an owl at the door
For a sentinel stood.

She had a son Jack,
A plain-looking lad,
He was not very good
Nor yet very bad.

She sent him to market
A live goose he bought,
Here, mother, says he,
It will not go for nought.

Jack's goose and her gander
Grew very fond;
They'd both eat together
Or swim in one pond.

Jack found one morning,
As I have been told,
His goose had laid him
An egg of pure gold.

Jack rode to his mother
The news for to tell;
She called him a good boy
And said it was well.

Jack sold his gold egg
To a merchant untrue
Who cheated him out of
The half of his due.

Then Jack went a–courting
A lady so gay,
As fair as the lily
And sweet as the May.

The merchant and the squire
Soon came at his back,
And began to belabour
The sides of poor Jack.

But old Mother Goose
That instant came in,
And turned her son Jack
Into famed Harlequin.

She then with her wand
Touched the lady so fine
And turned her at once
Into sweet Columbine.

The gold egg in the sea
Was thrown away then –
When Jack jumped in
And got it again.

And Old Mother Goose
The goose saddled soon
And mounting its back
Flew up to the moon.

I LOVE LITTLE PUSSY

I love little pussy, her coat is so warm,
And if I don't hurt her she'll do me no harm.
So I'll not pull her tail, nor drive her away,
But pussy and I very gently will play.

THE LION AND
THE UNICORN

The Lion and the Unicorn were fighting for the
    crown;
The Lion beat the Unicorn all round about the town.

Some gave them white bread, some gave them
    brown;
Some gave them plum cake, and drummed them out
    of town.

THE QUEEN OF HEARTS

The Queen of Hearts
She made some tarts,
All on a summer's day;
The Knave of Hearts
He stole the tarts,
And took them clean away.

The King of Hearts
Called for the tarts,
And beat the Knave full sore;
The Knave of Hearts
Brought back the tarts,
And vowed he'd steal no more.

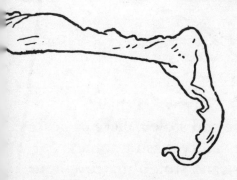

TAFFY WAS A
WELSHMAN

Taffy was a Welshman, Taffy was a thief;
Taffy came to my house and stole a piece of beef.
I went to Taffy's house, Taffy wasn't home;
Taffy came to my house and stole a marrow-bone.
I went to Taffy's house, Taffy wasn't in;
Taffy came to my house and stole a silver pin.
I went to Taffy's house, Taffy was in bed;
I took up the marrow-bone and flung it at his head.

PETER PIPER

Peter Piper picked a peck of pickled pepper;
A peck of pickled pepper Peter Piper picked;
If Peter Piper picked a peck of pickled pepper,
Where's the peck of pickled pepper Peter Piper
    picked?

THREE WISE MEN OF GOTHAM

Three wise men of Gotham
Went to sea in a bowl;
If the bowl had been stronger,
My story would have been longer.

HEY DIDDLE,
DIDDLE

Hey diddle, diddle,
The cat and the fiddle,
The cow jumped over the moon;
The little dog laughed
To see such fun,
And the dish ran away with the spoon.

LITTLE POLLY FLINDERS

Little Polly Flinders
Sat among the cinders,
Warming her pretty little toes.
Her mother came and caught her,
And whipped her little daughter
For spoiling her nice new clothes.

COCK-A-DOODLE-DOO!

Cock-a-doodle-doo!
My dame has lost her shoe,
My master's lost his fiddling stick,
And doesn't know what to do.

Cock-a-doodle-doo!
What is my dame to do?
Till master finds his fiddling stick,
She'll dance without her shoe.

Cock-a-doodle-doo!
My dame has found her shoe,
And master's found his fiddling stick,
Sing cock-a-doodle-doo.

Cock-a-doodle-doo!
My dame will dance with you,
While master fiddles his fiddling stick,
For dame and doodle doo.

JACK AND JILL

Jack and Jill went up the hill
To fetch a pail of water;
Jack fell down and broke his crown
And Jill came tumbling after.

Up Jack got and home did trot
As fast as he could caper;
Went to bed and bound his head
With vinegar and brown paper.

When Jill came in how she did grin
To see Jack's paper plaster;
Mother vexed, did whip her next
For causing Jack's disaster.

I SAW THREE
SHIPS COME
SAILING BY

I saw three ships come sailing by,
Come sailing by, come sailing by,
I saw three ships come sailing by,
On New Year's Day in the morning.

And what do you think was in them then,
Was in them then, was in them then?
And what do you think was in them then
On New Year's Day in the morning?

Three pretty girls were in them then,
Were in them then, were in them then,
Three pretty girls were in them then,
On New Year's Day in the morning.

One could whistle, and one could sing,
And one could play on the violin,
Such joy there was at my wedding,
On New Year's Day in the morning.

LADYBIRD, LADYBIRD, FLY AWAY HOME

Ladybird, ladybird, fly away
    home,
Your house is on fire, your
    children are gone;
All but one and her name is
    Ann,
And she crept under the
    pudding-pan.

HUMPTY
DUMPTY

Humpty Dumpty sat on a wall,
Humpty Dumpty had a great fall;
All the King's horses and all the King's men
Couldn't put Humpty together again.

CHARLEY, CHARLEY

Charley, Charley, stole the barley,
Out of the baker's shop.
The baker came out and gave him a clout,
Which made poor Charley hop.

DANCE TO
YOUR DADDY

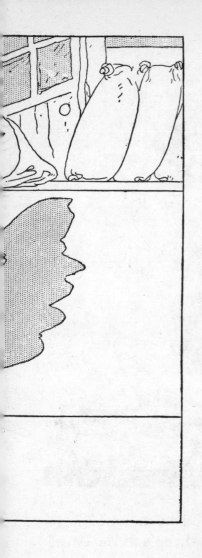

Dance to your daddy,
My little babby,
Dance to your daddy,
My little lamb,
You shall have a fishy
In a little dishy,
You shall have a fishy
When the boat comes in.

LITTLE BOY
BLUE

Little Boy Blue, come blow your horn,
The cow's in the meadow, the sheep's in the corn;
Where is the boy who looks after the sheep?
He's under a haycock fast asleep.
Will you wake him? No, not I!
For if I do, he's sure to cry.

JACK SPRAT

Jack Sprat could eat no fat,
His wife could eat no lean,
And so, between them both, you see,
They licked the platter clean.

81

SIMPLE SIMON

Simple Simon met a pieman,
Going to the fair;
Says Simple Simon to the pieman,
Let me taste your ware.

Says the pieman to Simple Simon,
Show me first your penny;
Says Simple Simon to the pieman,
Indeed I have not any.

Simple Simon went a-fishing
For to catch a whale;
All the water he had got
Was in his mother's pail.

HOT CROSS BUNS!

Hot-cross buns! Hot-cross buns!
One a penny, two a penny,
Hot-cross buns!
If you have no daughters,
Give them to your sons,
One a penny, two a penny,
Hot-cross buns!
But if you have none of these little elves,
Then you may eat them all yourselves.

DING, DONG, BELL

Ding, dong, bell,
Pussy's in the well.
Who put her in?
Little Johnny Green.
Who pulled her out?
Little Tommy Stout.
What a naughty boy was that
To try to drown poor pussy cat,
Who never did him any harm
And killed the mice in his father's barn.

LITTLE MISS MUFFET

Little Miss Muffet,
Sat on a tuffet,
Eating her curds and whey.
Along came a spider,
Who sat down beside her,
And frightened Miss Muffet away.

PUSSY CAT, PUSSY CAT,
WHERE HAVE YOU BEEN?

Pussy cat, pussy cat, where have you been?
I've been to London to see the Queen.
Pussy cat, pussy cat, what did you there?
I frightened a little mouse under her chair.

BOYS AND GIRLS, COME OUT TO PLAY

Boys and girls, come out to play,
The moon doth shine as bright as day,
Leave your supper, and leave your sleep,
And come with your playfellows into the street.
Come with a whoop, come with a call,
Come with a good will, or come not at all.
Up the ladder and down the wall,
A halfpenny loaf will serve us all.
You find milk, and I'll find flour,
And we'll have pudding in half an hour.

HERE WE GO ROUND THE MULBERRY BUSH

Here we go round the mulberry bush,
The mulberry bush, the mulberry bush,
Here we go round the mulberry bush,
On a cold and frosty morning.

This is the way we clap our hands,
Clap our hands, clap our hands,
This is the way we clap our hands,
On a cold and frosty morning.

·AND·EVERYWHERE·THAT·MARY·WENT·
·THE·LAMB·WAS·SURE·TO·GO·

MARY HAD A
LITTLE LAMB

Mary had a little lamb,
Its fleece was white as snow;
And everywhere that Mary went
The lamb was sure to go.

It followed her to school one day,
That was against the rule;
It made the children laugh and play
To see a lamb at school.

And so the teacher turned it out,
But still it lingered near;
And waited patiently about
Till Mary did appear.

Why does the lamb love Mary so?
The eager children cry;
Why, Mary loves the lamb, you know,
The teacher did reply.

TOM, TOM, THE PIPER'S SON

Tom, Tom, the piper's son,
Stole a pig and away did run;
The pig was eat, and Tom
    was beat,
And Tom went crying down
    the street.

MARY, MARY,
QUITE
CONTRARY

Mary, Mary, quite contrary,
How does your garden grow?
With silver bells and cockle shells,
And pretty maids all in a row.

THERE WAS AN OLD WOMAN WHO LIVED IN A SHOE

There was an old woman who lived in a shoe,
She had so many children she didn't know what to
   do.
She gave them some broth without any bread;
She whipped them all soundly and put them to bed.

OLD MOTHER HUBBARD

Old Mother Hubbard
Went to the cupboard
To fetch her poor dog a bone,
But when she got there
The cupboard was bare
And so the poor dog had none.

She went to the baker's
To buy him some bread,
But when she came back
The poor dog was dead.

She went to the joiner's
To buy him a coffin,
But when she came back
The poor dog was laughing.

She took a clean dish
To get him some tripe,
But when she came back
He was smoking a pipe.

She went to the fishmonger's
To buy him some fish,
But when she came back
He was licking the dish.

She went to the ale-house
To get him some beer,
But when she came back
The dog sat in a chair.

She went to the tavern
For white wine and red,
But when she came back
The dog stood on his head.

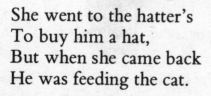

She went to the hatter's
To buy him a hat,
But when she came back
He was feeding the cat.

She went to the barber's
To buy him a wig,
But when she came back
He was dancing a jig.

She went to the fruiterer's
To buy him some fruit,
But when she came back
He was playing the flute.

She went to the tailor's
To buy him a coat,
But when she came back
He was riding a goat.

She went to the cobbler's
To buy him some shoes,
But when she came back
He was reading the news.

She went to the sempstress
To buy him some linen,
But when she came back
The dog was a-spinning.

She went to the hosier's
To buy him some hose,
But when she came back
He was dressed in his clothes.

The dame made a curtsey,
The dog made a bow;
The dame said, Your servant
The dog said, Bow-wow.

LUCY LOCKET

Lucy Locket lost her pocket,
Kitty Fisher found it;
There was not a penny in it,
Only ribbon round it.

LITTLE JACK HORNER

Little Jack Horner,
Sat in a corner,
Eating a Christmas pie.
He put in his thumb,
And pulled out a plum,
And said What a good boy am I.

THIS LITTLE PIG
WENT TO
MARKET

This little pig went to market,
This little pig stayed at home,
This little pig had roast beef,
This little pig had none,
And this little pig cried, Wee, wee, wee,
All the way home.

LITTLE BO-PEEP

Little Bo-peep has lost her sheep,
And doesn't know where to find them;
Leave them alone, and they'll come home,
Bringing their tails behind them.

Little Bo-peep fell fast asleep,
And dreamt she heard them bleating;
But when she awoke, she found it a joke,
For they were still a-fleeting.

Then up she took her little crook,
Determined her to find them;
She found them indeed, but it made her heart bleed,
For they'd left their tails behind them.

It happened one day, as Bo-peep did stray
Into a meadow hard by,
There she espied their tails side by side,
All hung on a tree to dry.

She heaved a sigh, and wiped her eye,
And over the hillocks went rambling,
And tried what she could, as a shepherdess should,
To tack again each to its lambkin.

THREE LITTLE KITTENS THEY LOST THEIR MITTENS

Three little kittens they lost their mittens,
And they began to cry,
Oh, mother dear, we sadly fear
That we have lost our mittens.
What! lost your mittens, you naughty kittens!
Then you shall have no pie.
Mee-ow, mee-ow, mee-ow.
No, you shall have no pie.

The three little kittens they found their mittens,
And they began to cry,
Oh, mother dear, see here, see here,
For we have found our mittens.
Put on your mittens, you silly kittens,
And you may have some pie.
Purr-r, purr-r, purr-r,
Oh, let us have some pie.

The three little kittens put on their mittens,
And soon ate up the pie;
Oh, mother dear, we greatly fear
That we have soiled our mittens.
What! soiled your mittens, you naughty kittens!
Then they began to sigh.
Mee-ow, mee-ow, mee-ow.
Then they began to sigh.

The three little kittens they washed their mittens,
And hung them out to dry;
Oh, mother dear, do not you hear
That we have washed our mittens?
What! washed your mittens! then you're good
     kittens,
But I smell a rat close by.
Mee-ow, mee-ow, mee-ow.
We smell a rat close by.

HUSH-A-BYE, BABY

Hush–a–bye, baby, on the tree top,
When the wind blows, the cradle will rock;
When the bough breaks, the cradle will fall,
Down will come baby, cradle and all.

THIS IS THE HOUSE THAT JACK BUILT

This is the house that Jack built.

This is the malt
That lay in the house that Jack built.

This is the rat
That ate the malt
That lay in the house that Jack built.

This is the cat
That killed the rat,
That ate the malt
That lay in the house that Jack built.

This is the dog,
That worried the cat,
That killed the rat,
That ate the malt
That lay in the house that Jack built.

This is the cow with the crumpled horn,
That tossed the dog,
That worried the cat,
That killed the rat,
That ate the malt
That lay in the house that Jack built.

This is the maiden all forlorn,
That milked the cow with the crumpled horn,
That tossed the dog,
That worried the cat,
That killed the rat,
That ate the malt
That lay in the house that Jack built.

This is the man all tattered and torn,
That kissed the maiden all forlorn,
That milked the cow with the crumpled horn,
That tossed the dog,
That worried the cat,
That killed the rat,
That ate the malt
That lay in the house that Jack built.

This is the priest all shaven and shorn,
That married the man all tattered and torn,
That kissed the maiden all forlorn,
That milked the cow with the crumpled horn,
That tossed the dog,
That worried the cat,
That killed the rat,
That ate the malt
That lay in the house that Jack built.

This is the cock that crowed in the morn,
That waked the priest all shaven and shorn,
That married the man all tattered and torn,
That kissed the maiden all forlorn,
That milked the cow with the crumpled horn,
That tossed the dog,
That worried the cat,
That killed the rat,
That ate the malt
That lay in the house that Jack built.
This is the farmer sowing his corn,
That kept the cock that crowed in the morn,
That waked the priest all shaven and shorn,
That married the man all tattered and torn,
That kissed the maiden all forlorn,
That milked the cow with the crumpled horn,
That tossed the dog,
That worried the cat,
That killed the rat,
That ate the malt
That lay in the house that Jack built.

A WAS AN APPLE
PIE

A was an apple pie,
B bit it,
C cut it,
D dealt it,
E eat it,
F fought for it,
G got it,
H had it,
I inspected it,
J jumped for it,
K kept it,
L longed for it,
M mourned for it,
N nodded at it,
O opened it,
P peeped in it,
Q quartered it,
R ran for it,
S stole it,
T took it,
U upset it,
V viewed it,
W wanted it,
X, Y, Z and ampersand
All wished for a piece in hand.

WHEN GOOD KING ARTHUR
RULED THIS LAND

When good King Arthur ruled this land,
He was a goodly king;
He stole three pecks of barley-meal,
To make a bag-pudding.

A bag-pudding the king did make,
And stuffed it well with plums;
And in it put great lumps of fat,
As big as my two thumbs.

The king and queen did eat thereof,
And noblemen beside;
And what they could not eat that night,
The queen next morning fried.

LONDON BRIDGE HAS FALLEN DOWN

London Bridge has fallen down,
Fallen down, fallen down,
London Bridge has fallen down,
My fair Lady.

Build it up with wood and clay,
Wood and clay, wood and clay,
Build it up with wood and clay,
My fair Lady.

Wood and clay will wash away,
Wash away, wash away,
Wood and clay will wash away,
My fair Lady.

Build it up with bricks and mortar,
Bricks and mortar, bricks and mortar,
Build it up with bricks and mortar,
My fair Lady.

Bricks and mortar will not stay,
Will not stay, will not stay,
Bricks and mortar will not stay,
My fair Lady.

Build it up with iron and steel,
Iron and steel, iron and steel,
Build it up with iron and steel,
My fair Lady.

Iron and steel will bend and bow,
Bend and bow, bend and bow,
Iron and steel will bend and bow,
My fair Lady.

Build it up with silver and gold,
Silver and gold, silver and gold,
Build it up with silver and gold,
My fair Lady.

Silver and gold will be stolen away,
Stolen away, stolen away,
Silver and gold will be stolen away,
My fair Lady.

Set a man to watch all night,
Watch all night, watch all night,
Set a man to watch all night,
My fair Lady.

POLLY PUT THE KETTLE ON

Polly put the kettle on,
Polly put the kettle on,
Polly put the kettle on,
We'll all have tea.

Sukey take it off again,
Sukey take it off again,
Sukey take it off again,
They've all gone away.

IF ALL THE WORLD
WERE PAPER

If all the world were paper,
And all the sea were ink,
If all the trees were bread and cheese,
What would we have to drink?

A FOX JUMPED UP
ONE WINTER'S NIGHT

A fox jumped up one winter's night,
And begged the moon to give him light,
For he'd many miles to trot that night
Before he reached his den O!
Den O! den O!
For he'd many miles to trot that night
Before he reached his den O!

The first place he came to was a farmer's yard,
Where the ducks and the geese declared it hard
That their nerves should be shaken and their rest so
    marred
By a visit from Mr Fox O!
Fox O! Fox O!
That their nerves should be shaken and their rest so
    marred
By a visit from Mr Fox O!

He took the grey goose by the neck
And swung him right across his back;
The grey goose cried out Quack, quack, quack,
With his legs hanging dangling down O!
Down O! down O!
The grey goose cried out Quack, quack, quack,
With his legs hanging dangling down O!

Old Mother Slipper Slopper jumped out of bed,
And out of the window she popped her head;
Oh! John, John, John, the grey goose is gone,
And the fox is off to his den O!
Den O! den O!
Oh! John, John, John, the grey goose is gone,
And the fox is off to his den O!

John ran up to the top of the hill,
And blew his whistle loud and shrill;
Said the fox, That is very pretty music; still –
I'd rather be in my den O!
Den O! den O!
Said the fox, That is very pretty music; still –
I'd rather be in my den O!

The fox went back to his hungry den,
And his dear little foxes, eight, nine, ten;
Quoth they, Good daddy, you must go there again,
If you bring such good cheer from the farm O!
Farm O! farm O!
Quoth they, Good daddy, you must go there again,
If you bring such good cheer from the farm O!

The fox and his wife, without any strife,
Said they never ate a better goose in all their life;
They did very well without fork or knife,
And the little ones picked the bones O!
Bones O! bones O!
They did very well without fork or knife,
And the little ones picked the bones O!

WEE WILLIE WINKIE

Wee Willie Winkie runs through the town,
Upstairs and downstairs in his nightgown,
Rapping at the window, crying through the lock,
Are the children all in bed, for now it's eight o'clock?

LITTLE TOMMY TUCKER

Little Tommy Tucker
Sings for his supper;
What shall we give him?
White bread and butter.
How shall he cut it,
Without e'er a knife?
How shall he marry
Without e'er a wife?

INDEX

A diller a dollar, 32
A fox jumped up one winter's night, 120-123
A frog he would a-wooing go, 18-21
A was an apple pie, 112-113
A wise old owl lived in an oak; 54

Baa, baa, black sheep, 16
Bobby Shafto's gone to sea, 48-49
Boys and girls, come out to play, 88

Charley, Charley, stole the barley, 78
Clap hands, clap hands, 40-41
Cock-a-doodle-doo! 68-69
Curley locks, Curley locks, wilt thou be mine? 15

Dance to your daddy, 79
Ding, dong, bell, 84-85

Early to bed and early to rise 51

For want of a nail, the shoe was lost, 29

Goosey, goosey gander, 17

Here we go round the mulberry bush, 89
Hey diddle, diddle, 66-67
Hickety Pickety, my black hen, 52-53
Hickory, dickory, dock, 8
Hot-cross buns! Hot-cross buns! 83
Humpty Dumpty sat on a wall, 76-77
Hush-a-bye, baby, on the tree top, 106

I do not like thee, Doctor Fell, 33
I had a little pony, 27
I love little pussy, her coat is so warm, 58
I saw three ships come sailing by, 72-73
If all the world were paper, 119

Jack and Jill went up the hill 70-71
Jack be nimble, 10
Jack Sprat could eat no fat, 81

Ladybird, ladybird, fly away home, 74-75
Little Bo-peep has lost her sheep, 102-103
Little Boy Blue, come blow your horn, 80
Little Jack Horner, 100
Little Miss Muffet, 86
Little Polly Flinders 68-69
Little Tommy Tucker 125
London Bridge has fallen down 116-117
Lucy Locket lost her pocket, 99

Mary had a little lamb, 90-91
Mary, Mary, quite contrary 94
Monday's child is fair of face, 34-35

Now I lay me down to sleep, 46

Oh where, oh where has my little dog gone? 42
Old King Cole 26
Old Mother Goose, when 56–58
Old Mother Hubbard 96–98
Oranges and lemons, 55

Peter, Peter, pumkin eater, 24–25
Peter Piper picked a peck of pickled pepper; 64
Polly put the kettle on, 118
Pussy cat, pussy cat, where have you been? 87

Rain, rain, go away, 15
Ride a cock-horse to Banbury Cross, 9
Ring-a-ring o'roses 47
Rub-a-dub-dub, 44–45

See-saw, Margery Daw, 22–23
Simple Simon met a pieman, 82
Solomon Grundy 37

Taffy was a Welshman, Taffy was a thief; 62–63
The Lion and the Unicorn were fighting for the crown; 59
The man in the moon 38–39
The Queen of Hearts 60–61
There was a jolly miller once, 6
There was a little girl, and she had a little curl, 11
There was an old woman who lived in a shoe, 95
This is the house that Jack built. 107–111
This little pig went to market, 101
Three blind mice, see how they run! 7
Three little kittens they lost their mittens, 104–105
Three wise men of Gotham 65
To market, to market, to buy a fat pig, 30–31
Tom, Tom, the piper's son, 92–93
Tweedle-dum and Tweedle-dee 50
Twinkle, twinkle, little star, 28
Two little dicky birds sitting on a wall; 54

Wee Willie Winkie runs through the town, 124
What are little boys made of? 36
When good King Arthur ruled this land, 114–115
Who killed Cock Robin? 12–14

Yankee Doodle went to town, 43

ACKNOWLEDGEMENTS

The sources for the pictures in this book are shown below. The editor
would like to extend special thanks to Miss Irene Whalley and the staff of
the Library, Victoria and Albert Museum, London and to Paul Dinnage;
in addition, to J. M. Dent & Sons Ltd, William Heinemann Ltd and
Frederick Warne Ltd. If the publishers have unwittingly infringed
copyright in any illustration reproduced they will gladly pay an
appropriate fee on being satisfied as to the owner's title.

Bewick, T. *The Figures of Bewick's Quadrapeds*, 1824. 42, 58: Bewick, T.
& J. *Select Fables*, 1820. 54: Brooke, L. L. *Nursery Rhymes, Songs and
Ditties*, 1916. 27, 72: Brooke, L. L. *Ring-a-Ring o'Roses*, 1976. 16, 17, 31,
38, 47, 53, 59, 68, 70, 76, 82, 101, 124: Carroll, L. *Through the Looking
Glass*, 1872. 50: Caldecott, R. *Painting Book*, 67, Folkard, C. *The Land of
Nursery Rhyme*, 1978. 11, 12, 13, 14, 26, 36, 37, 42, 69, 77, 80, 86, 90,
94, 104, 118: Hugo, Thomas. *Bewick's Woodcuts*, 43: *Mother Goose's
Nursery Rhymes and Fairy Tales*, 1892: 32, 41: Peake, M. *Ride a Cock
Horse*, 1940, 45: *Picture Book of the Nursery*, 1867. 13: Rackham, A.
Mother Goose Nursery Rhymes, 1975. 5, 7, 10, 23, 65, 74, 83, 85, 87, 88,
89, 95, 100, 119, 125: Rhys, E. and G. *Mother Goose's Book of Nursery
Rhymes and Songs*, 1910. 9, 64, 81: Robinson, C. *The Big Book of
Nursery Rhymes*, 1911. 1, 2, 8, 18, 20, 25, 29, 33, 34, 35, 40, 46, 49, 51,
56, 57, 58, 60, 63, 66, 78, 84, 88, 93, 96, 97, 98, 99, 102, 106, 107, 108,
110, 111, 114, 115, 120, 123: